FULL MOON HOLLOW
REPORTS MORE MISSING
PEOPLE PER YEAR THAN
CITIES 10 TIMES ITS SIZE.

FIFTEEN MILES OUTSIDE OF *FULL MOON HOLLOW*, KNOWN TO LOCALS AND TOURISTS AS "*AMERICA'S PARANORMAL CAPITAL*."

THREE HUNDRED YARDS OUTSIDE *WOLFSBANE CEMETERY*.

YOU TAKE THAT BACK! IT'S NOT MY FAULT.

NEVER SAID IT AS YOUR FAULT AT WE'RE SO FAR AWAY FROM ERYONE ELSE, PEYTON.

I JUST SAID THAT IF THE POPCORN HADN'T EXPLODED AND SET FIRE TO SCOUT-MASTER PHIL'S TENT, WE WOULDN'T HAVE BEEN BANISHED.

NO BLAMING.

YOU IMPLIED BLAME, TREY. IT'S NOT. MY. *FAULT.*

...GRUMBLE GRUMBLE STUCK WITH GRUMBLE GRUMBLE NERDS GRUMBLE GRUMBLE...

DOZENS OF PEOPLE SPONTANEOUSLY COMBUST EVERY YEAR--AND YOU KNOW THAT EVEN FREAKIER STUFF HAPPENS IN THE HOLLOW.

I COULD TOTALLY SEE THE POPCORN GOING... Y'KNOW... POP.

YOU DON'T BELIEVE ALL THAT "*AMERICA'S PARANORMAL CAPITAL*" GARBAGE, DO YOU? TV HYPE.

...GRUMBLE GRUMBLE GEEKS GRUMBLE...

CRAK

CRAK CRAK CRAK CRAK

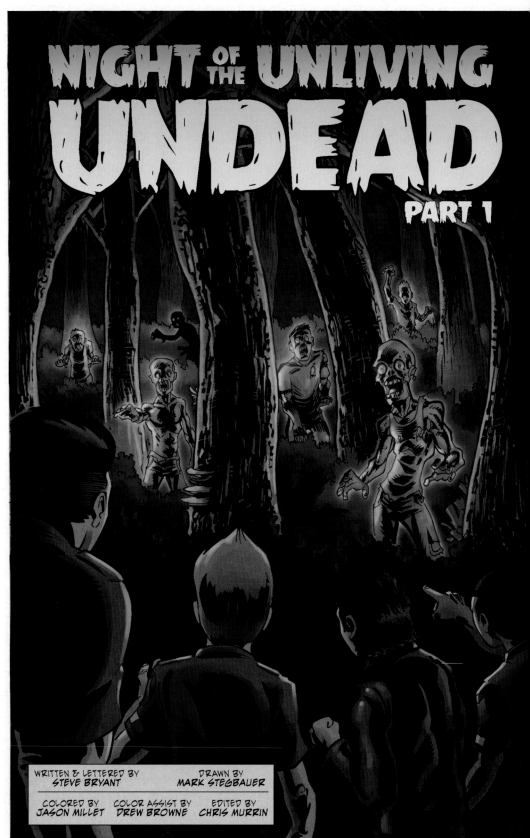

NIGHT OF THE UNLIVING UNDEAD
PART 1

WRITTEN & LETTERED BY
STEVE BRYANT

DRAWN BY
MARK STEGBAUER

COLORED BY
JASON MILLET

COLOR ASSIST BY
DREW BROWNE

EDITED BY
CHRIS MURRIN

Bryan Seaton - Publisher • Dave Dwonch - President • Shawn Gabborin - Editor In Chief • Jamal Igle - Vice-President of Marketing
Jim Dietz - Social Media Director • Chad Cicconi - eater of brain food • Colleen Boyd - Associate Editor

GHOUL SCOUTS #1, June 2016. Copyright Steve Bryant and Mark Stegbauer, 2016. Ghoul Scouts™ is a trademark of Steve Bryant and Mark Stegbauer. Published by Action Lab Comics. All rights reserved. All characters are fictional. Any likeness to anyone living or dead is purely coincidental. No part of this publication may be reproduced or transmitted without permission, except for review purposes. Printed in Canada. First Printing.

WAAAAGH!

EEEEEEEEIIIRRRRGGGH

GUYS? WAS THAT WHAT I THINK IT WAS?

EEEEIIIRRRGGGH

GUYS, THE *WALLS* ARE TOO STEEP! I CAN'T GET A HANDHOLD!

WHAK

WHA

KRAK

THUD

THAK

YOU GAIA SCOUTS DID *ALL RIGHT* BACK THERE.

YOU GUYS WEREN'T BAD YOURSELVES-- ESPECIALLY WITHOUT ANY *WEAPONS.*

MY NAME'S BECKY. BECKY PALMER.

I'M CHASE BANNON.

I'M ALEX DENT III.

BUT EVERYONE CALLS ME TREY.

AND I'M CLAUDIA RIVERA, BY THE WAY.

PEYTON. S'UP?

YOU LOOK *FAMILIAR.* DO I KNOW YOU?

NAH, I JUST HAVE ONE OF THOSE FACES.

SOME JAMBOREE, HUH? ARE YOU ALL THAT'S LEFT OF THE GAIA SCOUTS?

GHOUL SCOUTS BONUS FEATURE

CHASE

HERE'S A LOOK INSIDE MARK STEGBAUER'S *GHOUL SCOUTS* SKETCHBOOK!

THE NEXT FEW PAGES SHOWCASE THE VERY FIRST DRAWINGS OF OUR INTREPID SCOUTS!

MARK NAILED CHASE'S LOOK FROM THE FIRST DRAWING.

TREY'S APPEARANCE DEVELOPED OVER TIME. HE'S THE SMARTEST KID IN THE GROUP, BUT WE DECIDED TO STAY AWAY FROM "NERD" STEREOTYPES.

TREY

GHOUL SCOUTS BONUS FEATURE

PEYTON AND JEFF HAVEN'T CHANGED MUCH SINCE MARK FIRST DREW THEM.

AT FIRST, JEFF WAS GOING TO PLAY A LARGER ROLE ON THE TEAM.

IN FACT, THE ORIGINAL IDEA CALLED FOR THE TEAM TO BE CALLED THE **ZOMBOY SCOUTS**, AND TO CONSIST OF CHASE, TREY, PEYTON, AND JEFF.

PEYTON

IN THEIR SECOND ADVENTURE, THE **ZOMBOY SCOUTS** WOULD TEAM UP WITH A GROUP OF GIRLS WHO CALLED THEMSELVES THE **GHOUL SCOUTS**.

AS WE DEVELOPED THE STORY, WE REALIZED THAT THE TWO GROUPS SHOULD WORK TOGETHER FROM THE FIRST ISSUE.

JEFF

GHOUL SCOUTS BONUS FEATURE

AND HERE ARE THE BOYS' FINAL LOOKS. MARK MADE SURE TO
CREATE AN IMAGE THAT SHOWS THEIR RELATIVE HEIGHTS--VERY
IMPORTANT TO KEEP THE CHARACTERS CONSISTENT!

THE HONOR OF YOUR PRESENCE IS REQUEST...

HERALD
Lovecraft & Tesla

From John Re...

Tom Rogers

& Dexter We...

THE MADNESS CONTINUES THIS FALL
with "Tying the Knot"

YEAR...
ACTION! ARCOMIC...

MONTY
The Dinosaur

Action Lab's newest all ages adventure
100 million years in the making.

Making new friends starting in August 2016

Ask your local comic shop to order a copy,
or look for Monty The Dinosaur in Previews Magazine!

ALSO AVAILABLE: BOLTS #1 · HEROCATS #11 · I, MAGE #4 · VAMPBLADE V

LEGO

BUILD YOUR OWN STORY

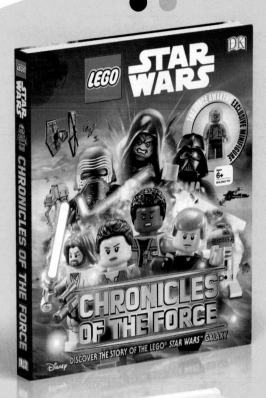

LEGO STAR WARS
THE FORCE AWAKENS EXCLUSIVE MINIFIGURE
Ages 6+ BUILDING TOY

CHRONICLES OF THE FORCE

DISCOVER THE STORY OF THE LEGO® STAR WARS™ GALAXY

Disney
DK

DC COMICS SUPER HEROES
LEGO CHARACTER ENCYCLOPEDIA
NEW EXCLUSIVE PIRATE BATMAN
Building 6+ Toy

LEGO NINJAGO Masters of Spinjitzu
CHARACTER ENCYCLOPEDIA
UPDATED AND EXPANDED
NEW EXCLUSIVE JAY MINIFIGURE
Ages 6+ BUILDING TOY
DK

e LEGO logo, the Brick and Knob configuration, the Minifigure,
and the NINJAGO logo are trademarks of the LEGO Group.
The LEGO Group. All rights reserved.
by DK Publishing under license of the LEGO Group.

All DC characters and elements
© & ™ DC Comics. (s16)

© & ™ 2016 LUCASFILM LTD.
Used Under Authorization.

Disney | LUCASFILM

 A WORLD OF IDEAS:
SEE ALL THERE IS TO KNOW

www.dk.com

LEGO
MARVEL
SUPER HEROES
TASKFORCE
BUILD SOMETHING
SUPER
LEGO.COM/MARVELSUPERHEROES
MARVEL
marvelkids co.
©2016 MARVEL
MARVEL
CAPTAIN AMER

THERE'S NO BLOOD.
AND NO BODIES. THERE'S
NO NEED TO THINK THE
WORST YET.

NIGHT OF THE UNLIVING UNDEAD

PART 2

SCOUT-MASTER PHIL'S TRUCK.

CHASE!

WRITTEN & LETTERED BY
STEVE BRYANT

DRAWN BY
MARK STEGBAUER

COLORED BY
JASON MILLET

COLOR ASSIST BY
DREW BROWNE

EDITED BY
CHRIS MURRIN

Bryan Seaton - Publisher • Dave Dwonch - President • Shawn Gabborin - Editor In Chief • Jamal Igle - Vice-President of Marketing
Jim Dietz - Social Media Director • Chad Cicconi - eater of brain food • Colleen Boyd - Associate Editor

GHOUL SCOUTS #2, July 2016. Copyright Steve Bryant and Mark Stegbauer, 2016. Ghoul Scouts™ is a trademark of Steve Bryant and Mark Stegbauer. Published by Action Lab Comics. All rights reserved. All characters are fictional. Any likeness to anyone living or dead is purely coincidental. No part of this publication may be reproduced or transmitted without permission, except for review purposes. Printed in Canada. First Printing.

SCOUTMASTER PHIL'S TRUCK... IT'S...IT'S...

I KNOW, BUDDY. I KNOW.

BUT THERE'S NO *BLOOD*. AND NO *BODIES*.

THERE'S NO NEED TO THINK THE *WORST* YET.

LOOK, CHASE. YOU'RE THE MAN WITH THE PLAN. NOBODY'S GONNA FOLLOW *ME*.

WE'VE GOT YOUR BACK, BUT WE NEED YOU TO HOLD IT TOGETHER.

CAN YOU *DO* THAT?

YEAH. YEAH, I CAN DO THAT.

KLAAAANG

COME WITH ME IF YOU WANT TO LIVE.

ARE YOU GUYS OKAY? WE GOT 'EM ALL.

WE'RE GOOD.

LET'S SEE WHAT'S LEFT OF OUR TOWN.

ONE MILE LATER.

AND OUT OF NOWHERE, THE POPCORN JUST *BURSTS* INTO FLAME!

THEN SCOUTMASTER PHIL COMES RUNNING OUT OF HIS TENT AND *FACEPLANTS* RIGHT IN THE MIDDLE OF CAMP!

HAHAHAHAHAHAHAHAHAHAHAHAHAHAHA

PEYTON *SWEARS* HE DIDN'T DO IT, BUT--

I *DIDN'T!*

SO JEFF DECIDES HE'S GOING TO SUCK UP AND TEACH PEYTON A *LESSON* AT THE SAME TIME.

HE COMES RUNNING ACROSS THE CAMP, *TRIPS* ON SCOUTMASTER PHIL, AND *COLLIDES* RIGHT INTO PEYTON, WHO *FALLS* INTO ME, AND WE ALL GO DOWN LIKE BOWLING PINS.

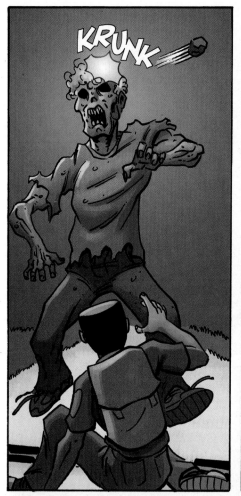

KRUNK

THANKS!

WHAM

WHAK

THUD

KLANG

CHASE! WE HAVE TO GO!

GUYS! THERE'S TOO MANY OF THEM! WE HAVE TO MAKE A BREAK FOR IT!

GHOUL SCOUTS BONUS FEATURE

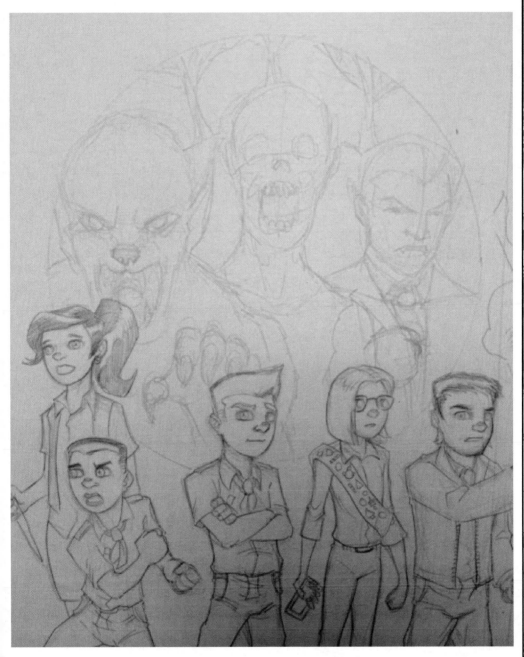

CONTINUING OUR LOOK INSIDE MARK STEGBAUER'S *GHOUL SCOUTS* SKETCHBOOK, MARK FIRST DREW BECKY AND CLAUDIA WHILE HE WAS DRAWING OUR INITIAL PROMOTIONAL IMAGE. WE WANTED TO SHOWCASE THE KINDSOF CREATURES THE *GHOUL SCOUTS* WOULD ENCOUNTER IN FUTURE BOOKS, SO THERE'S A WEREWOLF, A ZOMBIE, AND A VAMPIRE IN THE BACKGROUND.

GHOUL SCOUTS BONUS FEATURE

AND HERE'S HOW MARK'S FINISHED INK DRAWING LOOKS.
NOW *THAT'S* THE TEAM WE ALL KNOW!

GHOUL SCOUTS BONUS FEATURE

NEXT UP, COLOR ARTIST JASON MILLET WORKS HIS MAGIC,
ADDING EVEN MORE FORM TO MARK'S DRAWINGS! **WOW!**

THE HONOR OF YOUR PRESENCE IS REQUESTED.

HERALD
Lovecraft & Tesla

**From John Reilly,
Tom Rogers,
& Dexter Weeks**

E MADNESS CONTINUES THIS FALL
with "Tying the Knot"

5 YEARS
ACTIONLABCOMICS.COM

BUILD YOUR OWN STORY

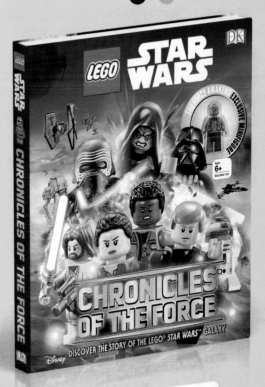

e LEGO logo, the Brick and Knob configuration, the Minifigure,
and the NINJAGO logo are trademarks of the LEGO Group.
The LEGO Group. All rights reserved.
by DK Publishing under license of the LEGO Group.

All DC characters and elements
© & ™ DC Comics. (s16)

© & ™ 2016 LUCASFILM LTD.
Used Under Authorization.

LEGO and the LEGO logo are trademarks of the LEGO Group. ©2016 The LEGO Group.
©2016 MARVEL

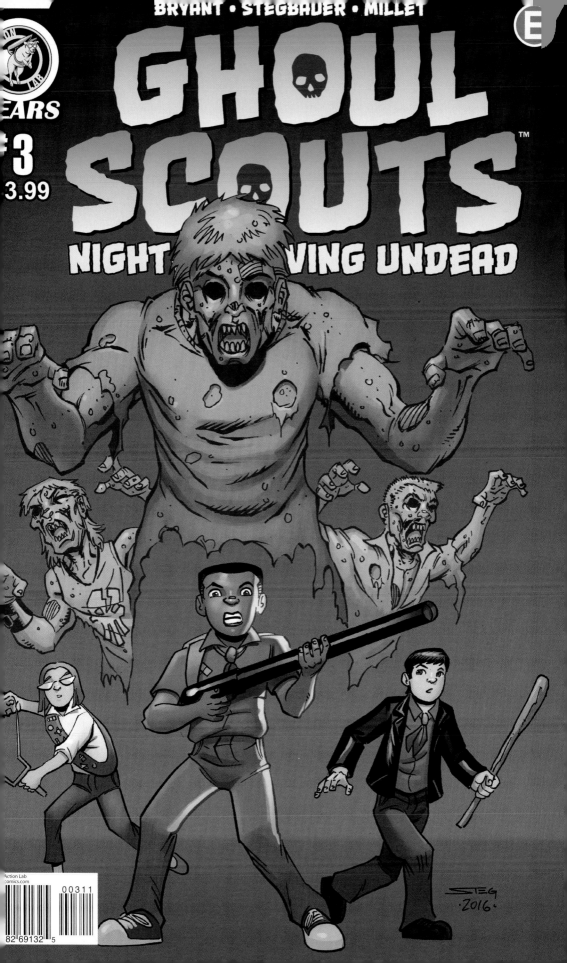

STRANGE CREATURES.
GHOSTLY APPARITIONS.

<SIGH> THAT'S ME.

I LOVE THAT SHOW.

YOUR FOLKS ARE LIKE THE COOLEST PARENTS *EVER!*

I EVEN MEMORIZED THE SHOW'S OPENING VOICEOVER...

"...STRANGE CREATURES. GHOSTLY APPARITIONS. THE MYSTERIOUS. THE UNEXPLAINED."

"JOIN CRYPTOZOOLOGIST DR. PAUL FORTE AND HIS WIFE, PARAPSYCHOLOGIST DR. ELLEN FORTE, AS THEY PEEL BACK THE CURTAIN OF THE UNKNOWN..."

"FOR THEY ARE..."

"...THE MONSTER CHASERS!"

"DUH-DUHT-DUUUUUHM!"

NIGHT OF THE UNLIVING UNDEAD PART 3

WRITTEN & LETTERED BY
STEVE BRYANT

DRAWN BY
MARK STEGBAUER

COLORED BY
JASON MILLET

COLOR ASSIST BY
DREW BROWNE

EDITED BY
CHRIS MURRIN

ryan Seaton - Publisher • Dave Dwonch - President • Shawn Gabborin - Editor In Chief • Jamal Igle - Vice-President of Marketing
Jim Dietz - Social Media Director • Chad Cicconi - eater of brain food • Colleen Boyd - Associate Editor

HOUL SCOUTS #3, August 2016. Copyright Steve Bryant and Mark Stegbauer, 2016. Ghoul Scouts™ is a trademark of Steve Bryant and Mark Stegbauer. Published by Ac-
n Lab Comics. All rights reserved. All characters are fictional. Any likeness to anyone living or dead is purely coincidental. No part of this publication may be reproduced or
transmitted without permission, except for review purposes. Printed in Canada. First Printing.

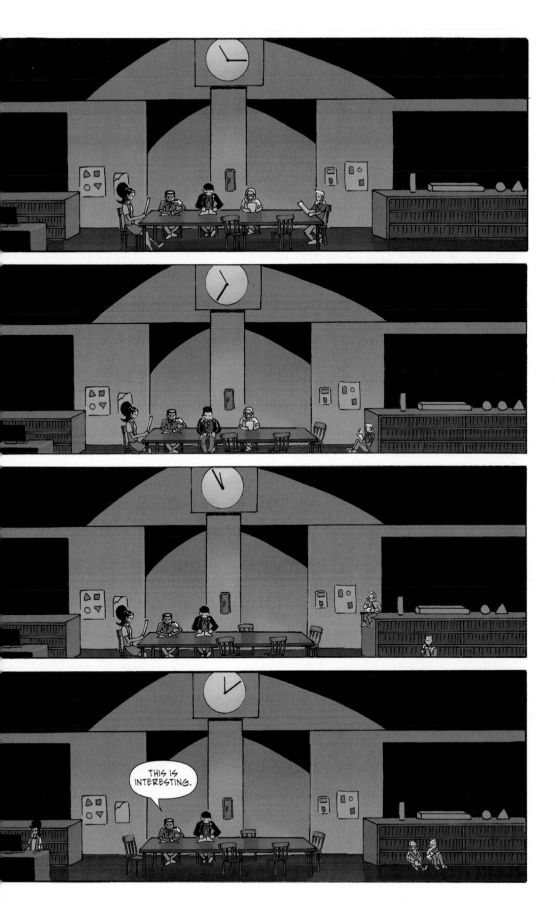

WHAT'S INTERESTING?

REMEMBER WHEN I SAID I THOUGHT ALL THE ZOMBIES WERE HEADED EAST?

CHECK *THIS* OUT!

Full Moon Hollow Herald

Thursday, October 9, 2014

EASTSIDE "HORROR HOUSE" DEFIES DEMOLITION

The historic Phillips house has survived multiple changes of ownership, World Wars, and now it's survived being torn down—after thirteen attempts.

By Alissa Fields

Built in 1865 by local author Howard Phillips, the mansion that bears his name has dominated the eastern skyline of Full Moon Hollow. In recent years, the house has fallen into disrepair and was finally scheduled to be torn down last April. In the time since the building was condemned, thirteen separate mechanical failures have postponed demolition. The latest one, oc- their decision to demolish the historic landmark. This development is only the most recent unexplained occurrence associated with the house since its construction.

After Phillips' son's death in 1957, the building was sold to renowned surgeon Hannibal Mason, who was later arrested after charges of patient abuse surfaced. Mason had no heirs, and upon his incarceration in 1966, authorities discovered the extent of the grisly experiments per- formed in his home.

"Mad Scientist Mason's House," as it had become known, was reopened in 1970 as The Pleasantville Home for the Criminally Insane. Reports of employee misconduct and patient mistreatment caused the Home to close its doors in 1975.

While it has remained unoccupied ever since, the house has been at the center of numerous unexplained phenomena, and has been featured on the television show Monster Chasers on si teen occasions.

Local N...
Page 2

MONSTROUS HERO MAKES ...
Sittyville's guardian spotted in Full Moon Hollow

This marks the second time that the paranormal investigator has been sighted in and around Full Moon Hollow. He was also seen at the 2014 Hemlock County Fair last month.

In both instances, when questioned about his presence, Full Moon Hollow Mayor Charles Difler delivered a firm "No comment." However, eye witness reports from carnival attendees state that the ghostly celebrity has an insatiable love of fried carnival foods. Concesssion sales reports substanti-

'he mysterious crime fighter known only as "Dr. Goyle" was spotted outside the Full Moon Hollow Cemetery Wednesday night.

ate this theory, citing a 300% increase over the previous year's sales.

Not much is known about the mystical adventurer, who remains famously private. He was featured twice the locally-filmed reality show Monster Chasers. Both appeared were unauthorize

With no concdence about the crusader's ly crusader's this reporter to the bottom mystery. Lo low-up fe day's Full Herald.

HAUNTED MAGIC EXHIBIT AT
Stage magician's collection of props featured at Full Moon Hollow Muse

It's only fitting that The most paranormal place on earth' play host to the opening exhibit of a long-lost collection of purportedly "haunted" stage magic props.

Museum curator Agatha Crowley said "Full Moon Hollow Museum is proud to debug the world tour of the 'Mysterious Life of aire' exhibit, of the 20th century's most mysterious performer."

"The Great Voltaire, as he was billed, was known for performing unexplainable acts of magic throughout his career. While the veracity of whether or not his magic was genuine pre tidigitation or mere a of misdirection rema hotly debated topic tween his fans and

nor cl s career

THAT JIBES WITH SOMETHING ELSE INTERESTING I *FOUND*.

DID YOU GUYS KNOW THAT FULL MOON HOLLOW IS HOME TO AN INCREDIBLY RARE--AND *POISONOUS*-- FLOWER?

"THE *WOLFS-SHADE*, A HYBRID OF WOLFSBANE AND DEADLY NIGHTSHADE WAS CREATED BY, GET THIS, RENOWNED SURGEON AND AMATEUR BOTANIST HANNIBAL MASON.

"IT'S POISONOUS AND IS REPUTED TO BOTH ATTRACT AND BANISH SELECT SUPERNATURAL CREATURES. AND IT'S ONLY FOUND IN *ONE* PLACE IN THE WORLD."

ANYONE CARE TO GUESS *WHERE* IT GROWS?

DU-UH. THE HORROR HOUSE.

WAITAMINUTE. *POISONOUS?*

I FOUND SOMETHING, TOO.

MISS CHUNG, WHAT DO YOU KNOW ABOUT THE *ZOMBOY SCOUTS?*

I HAVEN'T HEARD THAT NAME IN *YEARS.*

TALENT SHOW WINNERS
(l to r): Brad Bottig, Ana Hajarajanan

QUIZ BOWL WINNERS
(l to r): Leslie Winkle, Barry Kripke

LOOKS LIKE YOU WERE OUR AGE.

ZOMBOY SCOUTS: Protecting Full Moon Hollow from the unknown.

ZOMBOY SCOUTS: Protecting Full Moon Hollow from the unknown.
(l to r): Chaz Difler, Rudy Stevens, Dani Chung, Newt Flambach, Alissa Fields, Agatha Crowley

"PROTECTING FULL MOON HOLLOW FROM THE UNKNOWN."

IT'S LIKE YOU GUYS WERE DOING WHAT WE'RE DOING TONIGHT. WHAT'S THE STORY?

HONESTLY, I BARELY REMEMBER ANYTHING ABOUT IT.

WE WERE KIDS, LOOKING FOR ACTION AND *ADVENTURE.*

WE EXPLORED... RESCUED...

WHY IS IT ALL SO *FUZZY?*

THUMP

YOU LIKE THAT, BUTT-FACE? HOW 'BOUT SOME MORE?

THUD

FWOOSH

YEAH, YOU BETTER RUN!

PEYTON! ARE YOU--

RELAX, MAN, HE BARELY BROKE...

...THE SKIN.

LET'S NOT **READ** TOO MUCH INTO THIS.

I MEAN, SURE, IN MOVIES, AND TV AND BOOKS, A ZOMBIE BITE MEANS THAT YOU'RE GONNA DIE IN SOME HORRIBLE WAY AND THEN GET REBORN AS AN UNDEAD MONSTER INTENT ON EATING BRAINS, OR ENTRAILS OR WHATEVER, BUT...

BECKY'S **RIGHT.**

NOT HELPING, TREY.

SHE'S RIGHT THAT BOOKS, MOVIES, AND CERTAIN REALITY TV SHOWS SAY ONE THING IS GOING TO HAPPEN, BUT WHAT DOES **SCIENCE** SAY?

NOTHING. SCIENCE SAYS **NOTHING** ABOUT THIS. SO AS FAR AS I'M CONCERNED, WE OUGHTA TREAT THIS LIKE AN ANIMAL BITE.

MY MOM, MY DAD, AND MY THERAPIST TELL ME IT'S NOT MY FAULT.

I WANT TO BELIEVE THEM, BUT I CAN'T HELP BUT *WONDER* WHAT I COULD HAVE DONE DIFFERENTLY.

BUT EVEN WITH ALL THAT, MY LIFE DOESN'T SUCK.

I MEAN, I WOULDN'T WANT TO TRADE PLACES WITH PEYTON RIGHT NOW.

SORRY TO BUTT IN, I COULDN'T SLEEP.

ME, TOO.

I MEAN THAT I CAN'T SLEEP, EITHER.

AND I WOULDN'T WANT TO TRADE PLACES WITH PEYTON.

I CAN'T *IMAGINE* WHAT HE'S FEELING.

MY GRANDMA'S A BREAST CANCER SURVIVOR. SHE HAD SURGERY LAST YEAR, BUT I'M STILL *SCARED* IT'S GOING TO COME BACK.

EVERY DAY, I WAIT FOR BAD NEWS THAT MAY *NEVER* COME. I CONSTANTLY FEEL WORRIED AND HELPLESS.

I BET THAT'S HOW PEYTON FEELS RIGHT NOW.

IF NONE OF YOU GUYS CAN SLEEP, WHAT ABOUT PEYTON? WHAT IF HE *HEARD* US TALKING?

I HEARD YOU.

GHOUL SCOUTS BONUS FEATURE

ONE OF THE QUESTIONS WE'RE ASKED MOST IS **"HOW DOES AN ISSUE OF GHOUL SCOUTS GET MADE?"**

IT STARTS WITH A SCRIPT. WRITER STEVE BRYANT DESCRIBES THE ACTION FOR EACH PAGE.

SIXTEEN

Panel 1: The zombie standing over Trey is getting hit in the face with a rock. (It's been launched by Becky's slingshot)

1. SFX   Krunk

Panel 2: Becky, grinning, slingshot in hand, running past Trey, who is getting to his feet.

2. TREY   Thanks!

Panel 3: All 5 scouts running.

NO COPY

Panel 4: The scouts practically run into a group of zombies blocking their path. In the background, we can see that we're away from the residential part of town and are in the downtown/business part of town.

**All of the downtown shots should look like a post-apocalyptic movie: damage to buildings and cars, trash cans on fire, etc. No people.

NO COPY

FROM THERE, ARTIST **MARK STEGBAUER** DOES SMALL ROUGH DRAWINGS THAT GIVE HIM AN IDEA OF HOW THE PAGE WILL LOOK.

THESE ARE CALLED "THUMBNAILS." WHILE THEY'RE NOT AS SMALL AS YOUR THUMBNAIL, THEY'RE STILL SMALL--ABOUT 2X3 INCHES.

COMIC BOOK LAYOUT PAGE   TITLE Ghoul Scouts   ISSUE 2   PAGE # 16

NOTES

MOVE TREY DOWN ONE I

GHOUL SCOUTS BONUS FEATURE

FROM THERE, MARK RE-DRAWS HIS THUMBNAILS ON LARGER ART PAPER, CALLED BRISTOL BOARD.

THE BRISTOL BOARD IS 11X17 INCHES AND IS A HEAVY WEIGHT PAPER.

THIS STAGE IS CALLED "PENCILING," BECAUSE THE ART IS DRAWN WITH A PENCIL.

DUH.

SWORD OF THE EARTHMAN

"Like mainlining the Planet Hulk series while mashing your face into some classic issue of Hellboy."
- Annalee Newitz – io9

THE CRITICALLY
ACCLAIMED SERIES.
COLLECTED.

ON SALE NOW!

Is like Jack Kirby and Edgar Rice Burroughs love child, and that love child was awesome."
- Ben Rhodes - Fanbase Press

YEARS
ACTIONLABCOMICS.COM

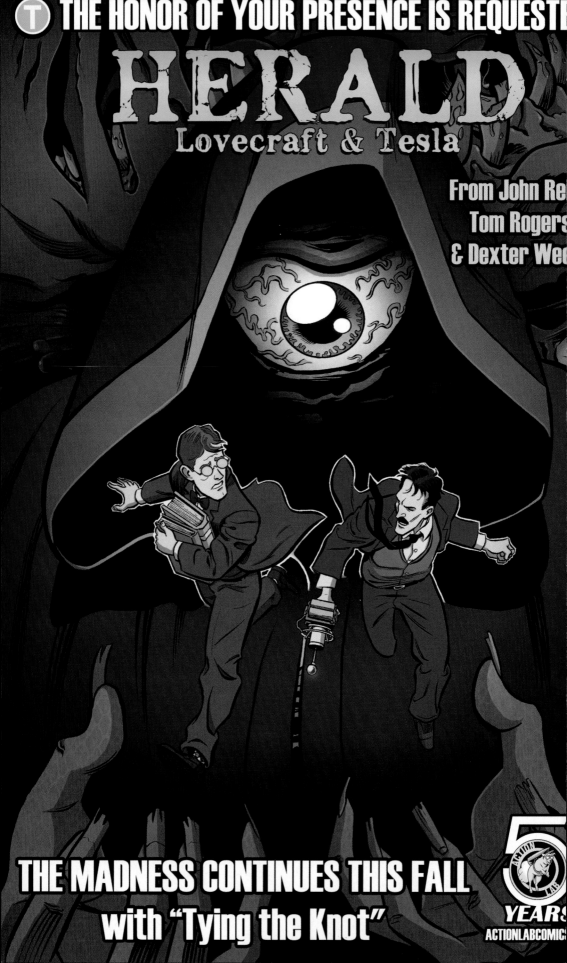

MONTY
The Dinosaur

Action Lab's newest all ages adventure 100 million years in the making.

Making new friends starting in August 2016

Ask your local comic shop to order a copy,
or look for Monty The Dinosaur in Previews Magazine!

Meet the new class.

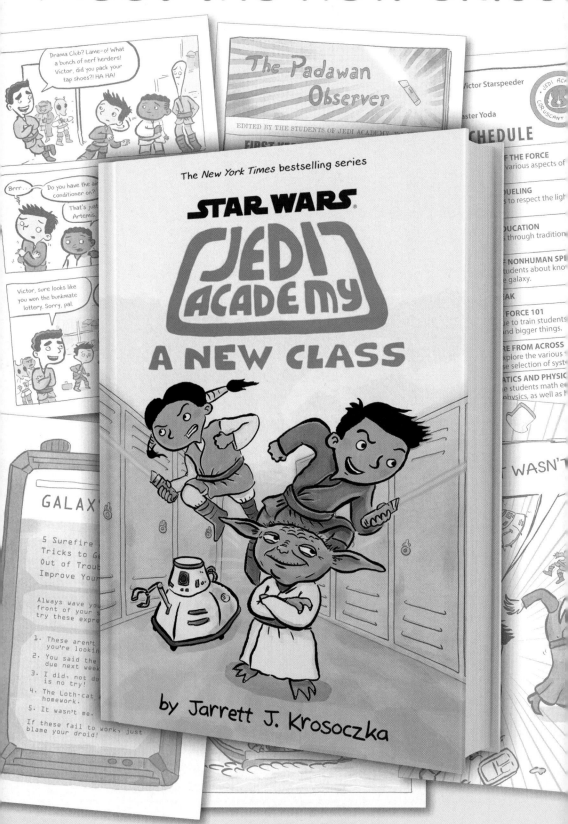

scholastic.com/starwarsjediacademy

© & TM Luca
SCHOLASTIC and associated logos are tra
and/or registered trademarks of Scho

SOMETHING'S HAPPENING
IN FULL MOON HOLLOW.
ADULTS IGNORE IT. OR
FORGET IT. OR THEY GO
CRAZY FROM IT.

ON THE TRAIL TOWARD FULL MOON HOLLOW'S FAMOUS "HORROR HOUSE."

I THINK WE'RE ALMOST THERE.

HEY, WERE YOU WRITING IN A JOURNAL BACK THERE?

I WAS DRAWING AND TAKING NOTES.

I STARTED CATALOGING THE ZOMBIES AND WHAT STOPS THEM. YOU KNOW...JUST IN CASE...

WANNA SEE?

YEAH!

NIGHT OF THE UNLIVING UNDEAD
PART 4

WRITTEN & LETTERED BY
STEVE BRYANT

DRAWN BY
MARK STEGBAUER

COLORED BY
JASON MILLET

COLOR ASSIST BY
DREW BROWNE

EDITED BY
CHRIS MURRIN

Bryan Seaton - Publisher • Dave Dwonch - President • Shawn Gabborin - Editor In Chief • Jamal Igle - Vice-President of Marketing
Jim Dietz - Social Media Director • Nicole DAandria - Editor • Chad Cicconi - eater of brain food

GHOUL SCOUTS #4, September 2016. Copyright Steve Bryant and Mark Stegbauer, 2016. Ghoul Scouts™ is a trademark of Steve Bryant and Mark Stegbauer. Published by
Action Lab Comics. All rights reserved. All characters are fictional. Any likeness to anyone living or dead is purely coincidental. No part of this publication may be reproduced
transmitted without permission, except for review purposes. Printed in Canada. First Printing.

WOW! I DIDN'T KNOW YOU COULD DRAW.

YEAH, I'VE ALWAYS DONE IT.

IT TAKES MY MIND OFF... Y'KNOW, LIFE AND STUFF.

WHOA.

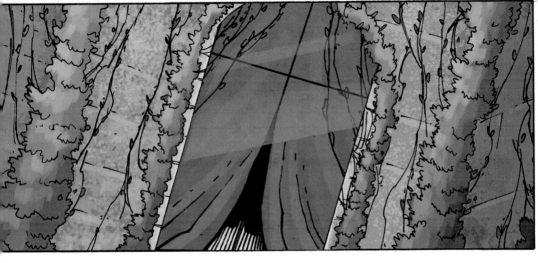

SLAM

EEEEERRGGH

KRAK

KLANG

WHAT NOW?

GREENHOUSE. ACCORDING TO THE PHOTO IN THE NEWSPAPER, IT SHOULD BE DOWN THAT HALLWAY.

WHAK

KLANG

THE GREENHOUSE SHOULD BE RIGHT DOWN THERE!

YOU KNOW WHERE THEY'RE *HEADED*, DON'T YOU?

KRUNK

WHAP

BAM

THERE IT IS!

ARE YOU KIDDING ME?

GROSS!

SLISH

QUICKSAND!

I'VE ALWAYS *HATED* THAT NICKNAME.

I NEVER DID ANY OF THOSE THINGS THE PAPERS SAID I DID.

IT WAS *THEM.*

THEY NEVER HELPED ME WHEN I WAS INSTITUTIONALIZED, EITHER.

BUT TONIGHT, THEY CHOOSE TO SET ME *FREE?*

WHY?

TO KEEP THIS OUT OF YOUR HANDS, OF COURSE.

IN FACT, I THINK I'LL KEEP IT FROM *THEM,* TOO.

YOU'RE GONNA BE ALL RIGHT, BUDDY.

DON'T YOU SEE? DISOBEYED THEM! I'M THE HERO HERE!

THEY'RE BEHIND IT ALL! THEY'VE BEEN HERE ALL ALONG.

CELL RECEPTION IS RESTORED. MY MOM'S COMING TO PICK ME UP. YOU GUYS NEED A LIFT?

EXCEPT FOR SOME MINOR BUMPS AND BRUISES, NO ONE AT THE JAMBOREE WAS HURT.

YEAH. EVEN *JEFF* MADE IT HOME SAFELY!

AND YOUR TEST RESULTS ALL CAME OUT *NORMAL?*

IF THERE WAS A ZOMBIE VIRUS IN MY BLOODSTREAM, THE FLOWER MUST HAVE KILLED IT.

THANKS TO HANNIBAL MASON. BURNING THAT FLOWER *SAVED* YOU AND THE WHOLE TOWN.

I'M JUST GLAD WE GAVE HIM THE COURAGE TO BREAK FREE FROM *THEM.*

WHOEVER *THEY* ARE.

I COULDN'T AGREE MORE. *SOMETHING'S* HAPPENING IN FULL MOON HOLLOW.

THE ADULTS TRY TO *IGNORE* IT. OR, IN THE CASE OF MS. CHUNG, *FORGE* IT. OR, LIKE MAD SCIENTIST MASON, THEY GO *CRAZY* FROM IT.

WE NEED TO FIND OUT WHO *THEY* ARE.

TOTALLY.

I'M IN.

ME, TOO.

HOW DO YOU GUYS LIKE THE NAME "*GHOUL SCOUTS?*"

END

LET'S CONTINUE OUR LOOK AT HOW GHOUL SCOUTS IS MADE.

AFTER THE DRAWINGS HAVE BEEN INKED, THEY'RE SCANNED AND SAVED AS COMPUTER IMAGES.

COLOR ASSISTANT **DREW BROWNE** SELECTS EACH SHAPE AND DROPS FLAT COLORS INTO IT.

YOU GUESSED IT--THIS IS CALLED "FLATTING."

GHOUL SCOUTS BONUS FEATURE

NEXT, COLOR ARTIST *JASON MILLET* WORKS HIS MAGIC.

JASON ADDS FORM BY DIGITALLY PAINTING SHADOWS AND HIGHLIGHTS.

ON THIS PAGE, HE ALSO ADDS IN SOME SIGNS THAT STEVE CREATED IN A SEPARATE COMPUTER FILE.

IT'S STARTING TO LOOK LIKE A COMIC NOW, ISN'T IT?

GHOUL SCOUTS BONUS FEATURE

AND FINALLY, THE BOOK GOES BACK TO STEVE, WHO PUTS ON HIS LETTERING HAT--

IT'S NOT A *REAL* HAT, OF COURSE. THAT'S JUST A SAYING, WHEN SOMEONE DOES DOUBLE DUTY.

NOW, WHERE WAS I? I GET A LITTLE CONFUSED-- WITH BEING UNDEAD, NOT HAVING A BRAIN, AND THE WHOLE DECOMPOSING THING.

NED, YOU IDIOT! YOU'RE JUST SUPPOSED TO SAY THAT THE BOOK GOES BACK TO STEVE, WHO ADDS WORD BALLOONS AND SOUND EFFECTS.
AND THAT THIS PROCESS IS REPEATED FOR EVERY PAGE IN THE BOOK.

KRUNK

THANKS!

SEE YOU NEXT ISSUE, KIDS!

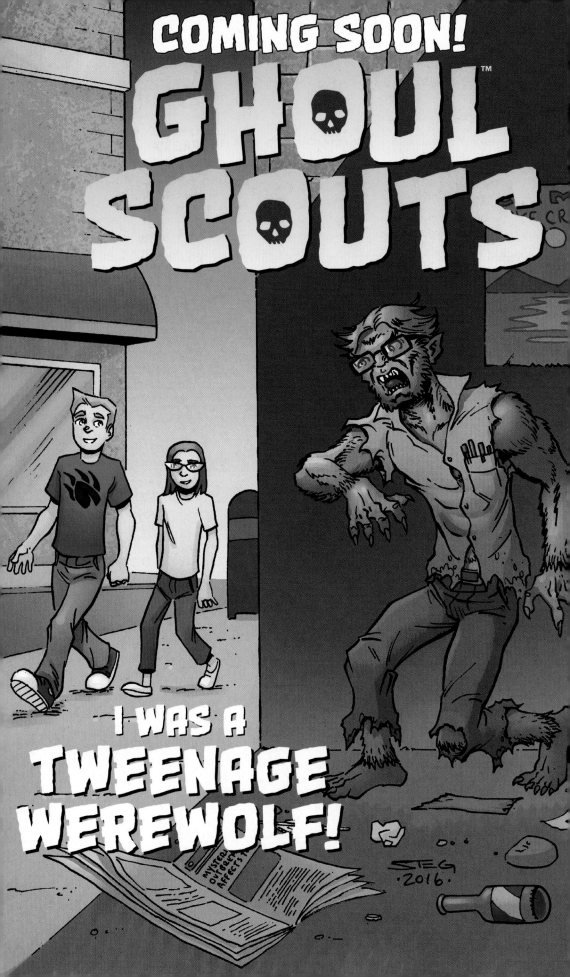

THE CREATORS BEHIND RAVEN: PIRATE PRINCESS AND STRAY!

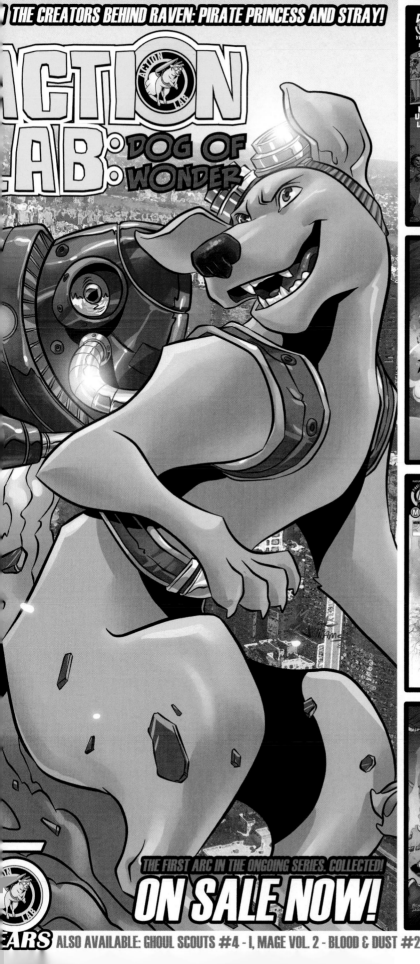

ACTION LAB: DOG OF WONDER

THE FIRST ARC IN THE ONGOING SERIES. COLLECTED!

ON SALE NOW!

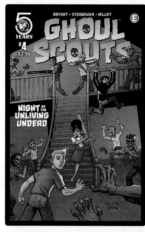

GHOUL SCOUTS
#4
$3.99
NIGHT OF THE UNLIVING UNDEAD

Mage
Adventure begins where science ends.

MARTIN ORNDORF MARTINEZ LEE NUTTALL 2 $3.99
BLOOD & DUST
THE LIFE & UNDEATH OF JUDD GLENNY

CHARLES BAND'S
PUPPET MASTER
BLOOD DEBT

ALSO AVAILABLE: GHOUL SCOUTS #4 - I, MAGE VOL. 2 - BLOOD & DUST #2 - PUPPET MASTER VOL. 4

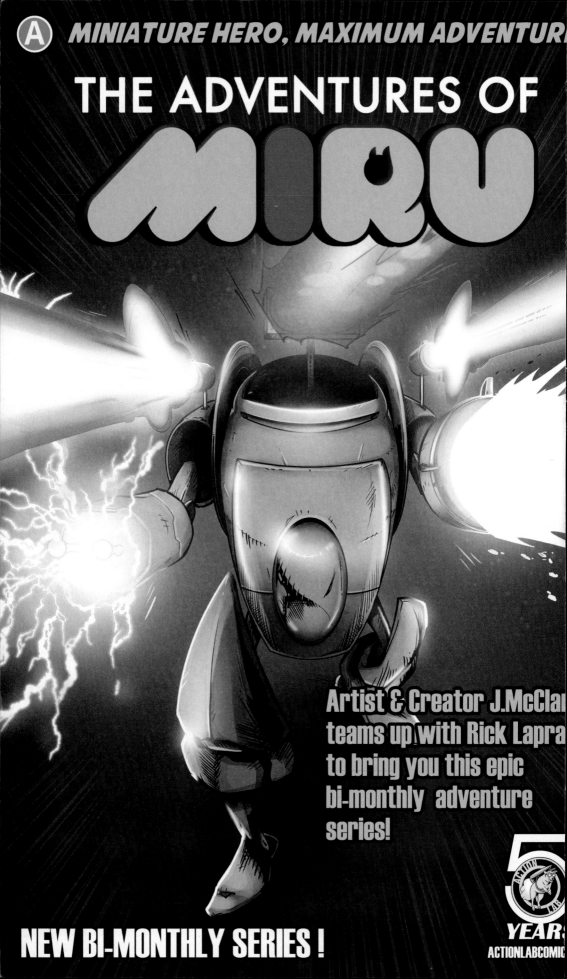

READ MORE NOW

Ghoul Scouts - Action Lab
www.actionlabcomics.com

00411

7 02382 69132 5

ACTIONLABCOMICS.COM